# The Lost Scarecrow

## ‘air’ and ‘are’

pair

air

scarecrow

scare

hare

rare

There was a scarecrow in the field next to the wood. It had a blue jacket, a pair of blue trousers and brown boots.

The scarecrow was sad because it did not scare the crows. Wellington barked at them, but he did not scare them either.

Then one day Wellington went to the field and the scarecrow was not there. The crows were flying in the air looking for it.

Wellington looked for the scarecrow. He saw

one of its boots in the corner of the field.

There was some straw by the fence.

A trail of straw went along the path into the wood. Wellington followed the trail looking for the scarecrow.

He saw a hare running between some trees. He saw a rare green woodpecker, but there was no sign of the scarecrow.

Then, suddenly, he saw a jacket and a pair of blue trousers next to a bush. They were the scarecrow's jacket and trousers.

Wellington peeped round the bush. He saw a fox and two little cubs in the straw in the scarecrow's jacket.

Wellington did not disturb them. He turned round to go back home. Just then he saw the scarecrow's head in the long grass.

The scarecrow did not look sad anymore. It had a smile on its face. It was looking after the fox cubs. It was happy.

Vowels:

| | |
|---|---|
| ai/ay/a-e: | trail day face |
| ee/ie: | between trees green peeped field |
| y/i-e: | flying by smile |
| ow/o/o-e: | scarecrow crows followed go home |
| oo/ue: | boots blue |
| oo: | wood looking woodpecker look |
| ow/ou: | brown trousers round |
| ar: | barked |
| er: | trousers either corner woodpecker after |
| or/ore: | for corner anymore |
| ur: | disturb turned |
| aw: | saw straw |
| air/are: | air pair scarecrow scare hare rare |
| ea: | head |
| soft c: | face fence |
| -y: | suddenly happy |

Verbs:

| | |
|---|---|
| -ed verbs: | turned followed looked barked peeped |
| Others: | was had did went were saw |

Exceptions: there because either one some sign they two